THEOP  ul
thistle s d
thistles, d
thistles If
Theophi d
unsifted),
where ... sixty thousand thistles
Theophilus Thistledown successfully sifted?

HOW much wood would a woodchuck chuck
If a woodchuck could chuck wood?

DOUBLE bubble gum blows doubly big bubbles.

IF a tottering tutor taught a Tongan tot
To tut-tut before that tot could utter,
What ought that Tongan tot to be taught
By this tottering tutoring tut-tutter?

SHALL Chef's chopper chappy chop chopped
chicken chipolatas or chop chocolate chips?

SISSY Smith lisps and lists. She lisps as she
talks and lists as she walks.

NINETY-NINE naughty knitted knick-knacks
were nicked by ninety-nine naughty knitted
knick-knack nickers.

CAN you imagine an imaginary menagerie
manager imagining managing an imaginary
menagerie?

LONGEST words in 10 different languages.

SWEDISH:

Sparvagnsaktiebolagsskensmutsskjutarefackf oreningspersonalbekladnadsmagasinsforradsf orvaltaren (manager of the depot for the supply of uniforms to the personnel of the track cleaners' union of the tramway company) — 94 letters.

GERMAN:

Donaudampfschiffahrtselectrizitetenhauptbet riebswerkbauunterbeamtengesellschaft — (the name of a club for minor officials of the office management of the steamboat electrical services) — 79 letters. This is not an everyday word, but Kraftfahrzeugreparaturwerkstatten (33 letters), which means a motor repair shop, is.

DUTCH:

Kindercarnavalsoptochtvoorbereidingswerkza amheden (preparation for a children's carnival procession) — 49 letters.

ENGLISH:

Webster's Third International Dictionary: pneumonoultramicroscopicsilicovolcanoconio sis (a lung disease) — 45 letters.

Oxford English Dictionary: floccinaucinihilipilification (estimating as worthless) — 29 letters.

ICELANDIC:

Haestarettarmalaflutningsmaour (a lawyer in the high court) — 30 letters.

PORTUGUESE:

Inconstitucionalissimamente (extremely unconstitutionally) — 27 letters.

FRENCH:
Anthropoclimatologiquement
(anthropoclimatologically — to do with people
and the weather) — 26 letters.

ITALIAN:
Precipitevolissimevolmente (as fast as possible)
— 26 letters.

SPANISH:
Subextraordinarisimo (extraordinary) — 20
letters.

JAPANESE:
Chi-n-chi-ku-ri-n (a very short person) — 12
letters.

TEN People who gave their names to everyday things.

Ladislao and Georg Biro — Ballpoint Pens
Louis Braille — Raised Writing for the Blind
Lord Cardigan — Woolly Coats
Rudolf Diesel — Motor fuel
Duke of Wellington — Welly boots
Charles Mackintosh — Rubberized Raincoats
Charles Rolls and
Frederick Royce — Expensive Cars
Earl of Sandwich — Butties
Henry Shrapnel — Shells that burst into small
pieces
Graf Ferdinand Zeppelin — Airships

TEN most common surnames.

ENGLAND AND WALES

1	Smith	6	Davis/Davies
2	Jones	7	Evans
3	Williams	8	Thomas
4	Brown	9	Roberts
5	Taylor	10	Johnson

USA

1	Smith	6	Miller
2	Johnson	7	Davis/Davies
3	Williams/ Williamson	8	Martin/Martinez/ Martinson
4	Brown	9	Anderson
5	Jones	10	Wilson

COMMONEST WORLDWIDE: Chang. At least 100 million, which is nearly twice the population of the United Kingdom.

LONGEST full name.

A man born in Germany and now living in the USA has a Christian name for every letter of the alphabet and a surname of 35 letters. Although his whole name contains 185 letters, he is normally known as Mr Wolfe + 180, Senior. His full name, however, is Adolph Blaine Charles David Earl Frederick Gerald Hubert Irvin John Kenneth Lloyd Martin Nero Oliver Paul Quincy Randolph Sherman Thomas Uncas Victor William Xerxes Yancy Zeus Wolfeschlegelsteinhausenbergerdorff, Senior.

The longest English surname (apart from hyphenated names, which are another story), is Featherstonehaugh (only 17 letters).

SHORTEST Surnames.

O, E and U are all genuine Oriental names. Many Western people have adopted one-letter names (perhaps to baffle computers?) but your author knew an English girl whose name really was Jo Em.

FAVOURITE Christian names.

These lists come from the Births column in *The Times*. The popularity of a name, however, depends on whether you count just the first name of each child (William) or all the names (William Henry Charles). Here are the top ten for "first names":

GIRLS		BOYS	
1	Alice	1	James
	Charlotte	2	Thomas
3	Sophie	3	William
4	Emma	4	Alexander
	Emily	5	Edward
6	Lucy	6	Charles
7	Katherine	7	Oliver
	Harriet	8	Nicholas
9	Alexandra	9	Christopher
10	Sarah	10	Henry/Robert

Here now are the "all names" top ten.

1	Elizabeth	1	James
2	Louise	2	William
3	Alice	3	Alexander
4	Charlotte	4	Thomas
5	Mary	5	Edward
6	Sophie	6	Charles
7	Rose	7	John
8	Alexandra	8	David
9	Lucy	9	Henry
10	Victoria	10	George

LANGUAGES

THE Ten Languages Spoken by the Most People.

1 *Mandarin Chinese:* 500m(million) North and East Central China
2 *English:* 320m UK, USA, Ireland, South Africa, Commonwealth
3 *Hindi:* 170m North Central India
4 *Russian:* 170m USSR (where 100 other languages are also spoken)
5 *Spanish:* 140m Spain, Central America and parts of South America
6 *Portuguese:* 120m Portugal, Brazil
7 *Japanese:* 110m Japan
8 *German:* 100m Austria, East and West Germany, Switzerland
9 *Bengali:* 90m Bangladesh, East India
10 *Arabic:* 80m Middle East, North Africa

MORE Languages.

BRAILLE

In 1829 a blind Frenchman, Louis Braille, invented a system of raised dots to help blind people to read.

THE MANUAL ALPHABET

This language helps deaf people to "speak" very quickly. Long ago workers in the noisy mills of northern England used this alphabet instead of shouting over the din of the machines.

MORSE

Samuel Morse's language can be sent over long distances using a key to open and close an electrical circuit. It can also be sent using flags or flashing lights.

SEMAPHORE

Semaphore uses flags to send messages.

Various people have tried to create international languages to help international understanding. Here are the four best known:

VOLAPUK — invented in 1880 by J M Schleyer;
ESPERANTO — invented in 1887 by L Zamenhof;
IDO — invented in 1900 by Louis de Beaufort and Louis Couturat;
NOVIAL — invented in 1928 by Otto Jesperson

Esperanto is the most popular.

TEN Biggest Countries in the World.

		sq km	sq miles
1	Russia	17,075,000	6,592,664
2	Canada	9,712,241	3,750,045
3	China	9,583,924	3,700,500
4	USA	9,324,934	3,600,500
5	Brazil	8,511,965	3,286,727
6	Australia	7,684,492	2,967,000
7	India	3,238,669	1,250,500
8	Argentina	2,772,487	1,070,500
9	Sudan	2,505,728	967,500
10	Algeria	2,381,740	919,662

Great Britain is Number 75 in the world line up with an area of 244,616 square kilometres, 94,450 square miles.

Russia and the Republics alone cover over 16% of the earth's surface; the Top Ten together cover nearly 60% .

TEN Smallest Countries in the World.

		Population	sq km	sq miles
1	Vatican City State	1,000	.44	.17
2	Monaco	26,500	1.8	.69
3	Macao	300,000	16.00	6.20
4	Nauru	8,000	21.00	8.10
5	Tuvalu	8,150	25.00	9.70
6	San Marino	21,800	61.00	23.50
7	Liechtenstein	27,000	157.00	61.00
8	St Christopher & Nevis	45,000	261.00	101.00
9	Malta	350,000	316.00	122.00
10	Grenada	95,000	331.00	128.00

TEN Countries with the Highest Population.

1	China	1,050,000,000
2	India	750,000,000
3	Russia & Republics	282,500,000
4	USA	238,800,000
5	Indonesia	170,500,000
6	Brazil	140,300,000
7	Japan	121,500,000
8	Bangladesh	103,500,000
9	Pakistan	101,000,000
10	Nigeria	96,000,000

United Kingdom, with a population of just under 57 million, is only number 16 in the list and its population is actually going down. 22% of the world's population live in China. On the other hand, some of the biggest countries in terms of land mass have quite small populations — Canada and Australia, for example.

TEN Most Densely Populated Countries.

		People per sq mile
1	Macao	68,065
2	Monaco	41,429
3	Hong Kong	13,963
4	Gibraltar	11,600
5	Singapore	10,946
6	Vatican City	5,882
7	Malta	3,033
8	Bermuda	2,816
9	Bangladesh	1,926
10	Bahrain	1,778

United Kingdom is fairly uncrowded at 605 people per square mile, but the Falkland Isles have only 0.41 of a person per square mile!

TEN Biggest Cities.

		Population
1	Tokyo/Yokahama, Japan	25,434,000
2	Mexico City, Mexico	16,901,000
3	Sao Paulo, Brazil	14,911,000
4	New York, USA	14,598,000
5	Seoul, South Korea	13,655,000
6	Osaka/Kobe/Kyoto, Japan	13,652,000
7	Buenos Aires, Argentina	10,750,000
8	Calcutta, India	10,462,000
9	Bombay, India	10,137,000
10	Rio de Janeiro, Brazil	10,116,000

London, Britain's capital, is number 13 in the league table with a population of 9,442,000 which is actually declining as more people move out to the country.

TEN largest states in USA.

	State	Area	
		sq km	sq miles
1	Alaska	1,518,800	586,412

2	Texas	691,027	266,807
3	California	411,047	158,706
4	Montana	380,847	147,046
5	New Mexico	314,924	121,593
6	Arizona	295,259	114,000
7	Nevada	286,297	110,540
8	Colorado	269,594	104,091
9	Wyoming	253,596	97,914
10	Michigan	251,493	97,102

TOP 10 countries with longest coastlines.

	Country	*Length of Coastline*	
		km	*miles*
1	Canada	90,908	56,488
2	Indonesia	54,718	34,000
3	Russia & Republics	46,671	29,000
4	Greenland	44,087	27,394
5	Australia	25,760	16,007
6	Philippines	22,540	14,006
7	United States	19,924	12,380
8	Norway	16,093	10,000
9	New Zealand	15,134	9,404
10	China	14,500	9,010
(12	United Kingdom	12,429	7,723)

Bearing in mind that the circumference of the Earth is 40,076km/24,901.8 miles at the Equator, Canada's coastline is more than twice that!

TEN Longest Rivers.

	River	miles	km
1	Nile (Tanzania-Uganda-Sudan-Egypt)	4,415	6,670
2	Amazon (Brazil)	4,007	6,448
3	Mississippi-Missouri (USA)	3,710	5,970

4	Yenisey-Algara-Selenga (Russia)	3,442	5,540
5	Yangtse-Kiang (China)	3,436	5,530
6	Ob-Irtysh (Russia)	3,362	5,410
7	Huang Ho (China)	3,001	4,830
8	Zaire (Congo, Angola)	2,920	4,700
9	Lena-Kiringa (Yakut)	2,734	4,400
10	Amur-Argun (China)	2,700	4,345

TEN Largest Oceans and Seas.

		sq km	sq m
1	Pacific Ocean	181,343,000	70,017,000
2	Atlantic Ocean	94,314,000	36,415,000
3	Indian Ocean	74,118,000	28,617,000
4	Arctic Ocean	12,256,000	4,732,000
5	Coral Sea	4,791,000	1,850,000
6	Arabian Sea	3,864,000	1,492,000
7	South China Sea	3,686,000	1,423,000
8	Caribbean Sea	2,753,000	1,063,000
9	Mediterranean Sea	2,515,000	971,000
10	Bering Sea	2,305,000	890,000

TEN Largest Lakes.

1	Caspian Sea (Iran/ Russia and Republics)	371,800	143,552
2	Superior (Canada/USA)	82,350	31,795
3	Victoria (Kenya/ Tanzania/Uganda)	69,500	26,834
4	Aral Sea (Russia and Republics)	65,500	25,290
5	Huron (Canada/USA)	59,600	23,012
6	Michigan (USA)	58,000	22,394
7	Tanganyika (Burundi/ Tanzania/Zaire/Zambia)	32,900	12,703
8	Great Bear (Canada)	31,800	12,278

| 9 | Baikal (Russia and Republics) | 30,500 | 11,776 |
| 10 | Nyasa (Malawi/Mozambique/Tanzania) | 29,600 | 11,429 |

TEN Highest Waterfalls.

	Waterfall	Location	m	ft
1	Angel	Venezuela	979	3,212
2	Tugela	South Africa	948	3,110
3	Utigard	Norway	800	2,625
4	Mongefossen	Norway	774	2,540
5	Yosemite	USA	739	2,425
6	Ostre Mardola Foss	Norway	657	2,154
7	Tyssestrengame	Norway	646	2,120
8	Cuquenan	Venezuela	610	2,000
9	Sutherland	New Zealand	580	1,904
10	Kjellfossen	Norway	561	1,841

COUNTRIES where you can expect to live longest.

Life expectancy depends on climate, diet, health care and, of course, wars and famines. When, as a result of improvements in medicine, more babies and young children survive, the average life expectancy rises. Almost everywhere, however, women have a higher life expectancy than men.

MEN
1	Iceland	74 years
2	Japan/Sweden	73 years
4	Norway, Turkey	72 years
6	Australia, Denmark	71 years

| 8 | Canada, France, Greece, Italy, Spain, Switzerland, USA | 70 years |

Great Britain ties with Albania with a life expectancy for men of 68 years.

WOMEN

1	Iceland	80 years
2	Japan/Sweden/Norway/Finland	79 years
6	Australia, France, USA	78 years
9	Canada, Denmark	77 years

Great Britain ties with Greece, Czechoslovakia, with Russia, Hungary and the Irish Republic with a life expectancy for women of 74 years.

COUNTRIES where you are likeliest to die young.

In these countries a great many babies and young children die every year, which lowers the average life expectancy. Notice that even in these countries women can still expect to live longer than men, despite the risks of child-birth.

MEN

1	Ethiopia	38 years
2	Guinea, Gambia, North Yemen	39 years
5	Angola, Burundi	40 years
7	Burkina Faso, Malawi, Mali, Mauritania, Niger, Senegal, Somalia	41 years

WOMEN

1	North Yemen	40 years
2	Ethiopia	41 years
3	Afghanistan, Angola, Guinea, Burundi, Gambia, Bhutan, Nepal	43 years
10	Burkina Faso, Mali, Malawi, Mauritania, Niger, Senegal, Liberia	44 years

TEN longest place names in the world.

	Name	Letters	Meaning	Location
1	Krung Thep Mahanakhon Bovorn Ratanakosin Mahintharayutthaya Mahadilok pop Noparatratchathani Burirom Udomratchanivetmahasathan Amornpiman Avatarnsathit Sakkathattiyavisnukarmprasit	167	Poetic name for Bangkok	Thailand
2	Taumatawhakatangihangakoauauotama-teaturipukakapikimaungahoronukupokai-whenuakitanatahu	85	Maori name for a hill	NZ
3	Gorsafawddachaidraigddanheddogleddol-lônpenrhynareurdraethceredigion	67	Name of rail-way station	Wales
4	Llanfairpwllgwyngyllgogerychwyrndrobwll-llantysiliogogogoch	58	Place name	Wales
5	El Pueblo de Nuestra Senora la Reina de los Angeles de la Porciuncula	57	Los Angeles	USA
6	Chargoggagoggmanchauggagoggchau-bunagungamaugg	45	A lake	USA
7	Lower North Branch Little Southwest Miramichi	40	A river	Canada
	Villa Real de la Santa Fe de San Francisco de Asis	40	San Francisco	USA
9	Te Whakatakanga-o-te-ngarehu-o-te-ahi-a-Tametea	38	Hammer Springs	NZ
10	Loch Airidh Mhic Fhiomlaidh Dhuibh	31	A loch	Scotland

TEN Fastest Mammals.

		Recorded Speed	
		kph	mph
1	Cheetah	104	65
2	Pronghorn Antelope	88	55
3	Mongolian Gazelle	80	50
	Springbok	80	50
5	Thompson's Gazelle	75	47
	Grant's Gazelle	75	47
7	Brown Hare	72	45
8	Horse	69	43
9	Red Deer	67	42
	Greyhound	67	42

By comparison, a human athlete runs a four-minute mile at an average of just 15 mph.

TEN Fastest Fish.

1	Sailfish	110	68
2	Marlin	80	50
3	Wahoo	78	48
4	Tunny	74	46
5	Bluefish Tuna	70	44
6	Great Blue Shark	69	43
7	Bonefish	64	40
	Swordfish	64	40
9	Four-winged Flying Fish	56	35
	Tarpon	56	35

35 knots (40 mph/65 kph) is good going for most ships.

TEN Fastest Birds.

		kph	mph
1	Spinetail Swift	171	106
2	Frigate Bird	153	95
3	Spur-winged Goose	142	88
4	Red-breasted Merganser	129	80
5	White-rumped Swift	124	77
6	Canvasback Duck	116	72
7	Eider Duck	113	70
8	Teal	109	68
9	Pintail Duck	105	65
	Mallard	105	65

RAREST Animals in captivity.

	Wild	Zoos
Golden Lion Tamarin	500	300
Giant Panda	500	50
Lion-tailed Macaque	500	300
Przewalski's Horse	10	500
Northern White Rhino	500	16
Arabian Oryx	40	300
Laysan Duck	150	200
Hawaiian Goose	1000	1000
Nduk Eagle Owl	200	100

DOGS
TOP Ten Breeds in the USA
Registered by the American Kennel Club.

1	Cocker Spaniel	111,636
2	Labrador Retriever	91,107
3	Poodle	78,600
4	Golden Retriever	64,269
5	German Shepherd (Alsatian)	58,422
6	Rottweiler	51,291
7	Chow Chow	50,150
8	Dachshund	44,305
9	Beagle	43,314
10	Miniature Schnauzer	42,175

TOP Ten Breeds in Britain
Registered by the Kennel Club.

1	Yorkshire Terrier	25,665
2	Labrador Retriever	24,456
3	German Shepherd (Alsatian)	18,908
4	West Highland White Terrier	18,688
5	Cavalier King Charles Spaniel	16,823
6	Golden Retriever	15,983
7	Cocker Spaniel	12,866
8	English Springer Spaniel	11,349
9	Staffordshire Bull Terrier	7,609
10	Boxer	6,949

Jack Russell Terriers were No. 2 in a recent Gallup National Dog Survey, and the Kennel Club, now recognises the breed.

MOST Popular Dogs' Names.

GREAT BRITAIN	USA
1 Ben	1 Lady
2 Sam	2 King
3 Susie	3 Duke
4 Benji	4 Peppy/Pepe
5 Max	5 Prince
6 Lucy	6 Pepper
7 Kim	7 Snoopy
8 Lady	8 Princess
9 Shelley	9 Heidi
10 Judy	10 Sam/Coco

There are lots of unusual names around. Try compiling some for yourself. A Suffolk family call their dogs after railway stations. They started with Euston and Paddington and now own a Kings Cross.

CATS

All cats, they say, answer to Puss or Kitty, but a British cat food firm performed a survey of cats' names. **Here are the top ten:**

1 Sooty		6 Kitty
2 Tiger		7 Lucky
3 Smoky		8 Susie/Suzie
4 Tigger		9 Fluffy
5 Whisky		10 Snowy

TEN Real Life Dog Stars, in no particular order of merit or importance.

Greyfriars Bobby guarded his master's grave in Greyfriars Churchyard, Edinburgh and was awarded the freedom of the city. Walt Disney made a film about him.

Rin Tin Tin starred in many movies and was buried in the pets' cemetery in Paris, where his name is pronounced Ran Tan Tan.

Petra, an Alsatian cross, was the star of BBC TV's Blue Peter and had a statue erected in her memory.

Goldie the golden retriever, another Blue Peter star, always had her birthday party on TV and gave birth (not on TV) to two litters of puppies.

Tim patrolled Paddington Station with a collecting box in aid of widows and orphans. After his death in 1902 he was stuffed and went on to collect large sums until the moths got him.

Chance, a bull terrier/mastiff cross, worked with the Fire Brigade in London and saved several lives before being killed by a collapsing wall in a blazing building. He too was stuffed and put on show in aid of firemen's charities. It is said that his ghost can be seen in the flames of burning buildings.

Bobbie, a collie, was lost by his owners while they were on holiday in Indiana, USA. He turned up at the family home in Oregon 6 months later after a trek of 2000 miles. Yes, it was the same dog, and he had crossed the Rocky Mountains in the depths of winter.

Bluey, an Australian farm dog, worked with cattle and sheep for nearly 20 years and was put to sleep in 1939 at age 29 — old enough to win him a place in the Guiness Book of records.

Emma, a chocolate Labrador, was the guide dog of Sheila Hockin. Sheila told their story in a book entitled "Emma and I".

Flush, the spaniel of the poet Elizabeth Barrett Browning, had an eventful life which included being kidnapped and held to ransom. Elizabeth wrote poems about her pet and Virginia Woolf wrote *Flush: a Biography*.

TOP Ten Olympic Gold Medallists.

1   Ray C. Ewry (USA) Athletics
    1900, 1904, 1906, 1908   10
2   Larissa Latynina (USSR) Gymnastics
    1956, 1960, 1964   9
    Paavo Nurmi (Finland) Athletics
    1920, 1924, 1928   9
    Mark Spitz (USA) Swimming
    1968, 1972   9
5   Sawao Kato (Japan) Gymnastics
    1968, 1972, 1976   8
6   Nikolai Andrianov (USSR) Gymnastics
    1972, 1976, 1980   7
    Boris Shakhlin (USSR) Gymnastics
    1956, 1960, 1964   7
    Vera Caslavska (Czechoslovakia)
    Gymnastics, 1960, 1964, 1968   7
    Viktor Chukarin (USSR) Gymnastics
    1952, 1956   7
    Aladar Gerevich (Hungary) Fencing
    1932, 1936, 1948, 1952, 1956, 1960*   7

*There were no Olympics in 1940 or 1944 because of World War II.

TOP Ten Summer Olympics gold medal winners, 1896-1988.

	Country	Number of Medals
1	United States	756
2	USSR	395
3	United Kingdom	173
4	W. Germany	157
5	France	153
6	E. Germany	153
7	Italy	147
8	Sweden	131
9	Hungary	124
10	Finland	97

TOP Ten Winter Olympics gold medal winners, 1924-1988.

	Country	Number of Medals
1	USSR	79
2	Norway	54
3	United States	42
4	East Germany	39
5	Sweden	36
6	Finland	33
7	Austria	28
8	West Germany	26
9	Switzerland	23
10	Canada	14
	Italy	14

SOCCER

World Cup Winners and Runners-Up since the competition began.

1930 Uruguay 4 Argentina 2
1934 Italy 2 Czechoslovakia 1
1938 Italy 4 Hungary 2
(no contest during the Second World War)
1950 Uruguay 2 Brazil 1
1954 W Germany 3 Hungary 2

1958	Brazil 5 Sweden 2
1962	Brazil 3 Czechoslovakia 1
1966	England 4 W Germany 2
1970	Brazil 4 Italy 1
1974	W Germany 2 Netherlands 1
1978	Argentina 3 Netherlands 1
1982	Italy 3 W Germany 1
1986	Argentina 3 W Germany 2
1990	W Germany 1 Argentina 0

MOTOR RACING

World Champions.

Year	Winner	Car
1951	Juan Fangio (Argentina)	Alfa Romeo
1952	Alberto Ascari (Italy)	Ferrari
1953	Alberto Ascari (Italy)	Ferrari
1954	Juan Fangio (Argentina)	Maserati/Mercedes
1955	Juan Fangio (Argentina)	Mercedes-Benz
1956	Juan Fangio (Argentina)	Lancia-Ferrari
1957	Juan Fangio (Argentina)	Maserati
1958	Mike Hawthorn (UK)	Ferrari
1959	Jack Brabham (Australia)	Cooper-Climax
1960	Jack Brabham (Australia)	Cooper-Climax
1961	Phil Hill (USA)	Ferrari
1962	Graham Hill (UK)	BRM
1963	Jim Clark (UK)	Lotus-Climax
1964	John Surtees (GB)	Ferrari

Year	Driver	Car
1965	Jim Clark (GB)	Lotus-Climax
1966	Jack Brabham (Australia)	Brabham-Repco
1967	Denny Hulme (New Zealand)	Brabham-Repco
1968	Graham Hill (UK)	BRM
1969	Jackie Stewart (UK)	Matra-Ford
1970	Jochen Rindt (Austria)	Lotus-Ford
1971	Jackie Stewart (GB)	Tyrell-Ford
1972	Emerson Fittipaldi (Brazil)	Lotus-Ford
1973	Jackie Stewart (UK)	Tyrrell-Ford
1974	Emerson Fittipaldi (Brazil)	Lotus-Ford
1975	Niki Lauda (Austria)	Ferrari
1976	James Hunt (UK)	McLaren-Ford
1977	Niki Lauda (Austria)	Ferrari
1978	Mario Andretti (USA)	Lotus-Ford
1979	Jody Schechter (South Africa)	Ferrari
1980	Alan Jones (Australia)	Williams-Ford
1981	Nelson Piquet (Brazil)	Brabham-Ford
1982	Keke Rosberg (Finland)	Williams-Ford
1983	Nelson Piquet (Brazil)	Brabham-BMW
1984	Niki Lauda (Austria)	McLaren-TAG
1985	Alain Prost (France)	McLaren-TAG

1986	Alain Prost (France)	McLaren-TAG
1987	Nelson Piquet (Brazil)	Williams-Honda
1988	Ayrton Senna (Brazil)	McLaren-Honda
1989	Alain Prost (France)	McLaren-TAG
1990	Ayrton Senna (Brazil)	McLaren-Honda
1991	Alain Prost (France)	McLaren-TAG
1992	Nigel Mansell (United Kingdom)	Williams-Renault

Most Successful Drivers.

World Championships		
5	**3**	**2**
Fangio	Brabham	Clark
	Stewart	Ascari
	Lauda	Graham Hill
	Piquet	Fittipaldi
	Prost	
	Senna	

Ten Bestselling Albums Worldwide.

1 Thriller *Michael Jackson*
2 Saturday Night Fever *Various*
3 Grease Soundtrack *Various*
4 Sergeant Pepper's Lonely Hearts Club Band *The Beatles*
5 Bridge Over Troubled Water *Simon and Garfunkel*
6 Born in the USA *Bruce Springsteen*
7 The Sound of Music Soundtrack *Various*
8 Abbey Road *The Beatles*
9 Rumours *Fleetwood Mac*
10 Brothers in Arms *Dire Straits*

Albums sell in huge numbers: Thriller has sold over 40,000,000 and is still doing well.

TEN Bestselling Singles Worldwide.

1 White Christmas *Bing Crosby* 30,000,000
2 Rock Around the Clock *Bill Haley and the Comets* 17,000,000
3 I Want to Hold Your Hand *The Beatles* 12,000,000
4 It's Now or Never *Elvis Presley* 10,000,000
5 Hound Dog/Don't Be Cruel *Elvis Presley* 9,000,000
   Diana *Paul Anka* 9,000,000
7 Hey Jude *The Beatles* 8,000,000
   I'm a Believer *The Monkees* 8,000,000
9 We Are the World *USA for Africa* 7,000,000
   Can't Buy Me Love *The Beatles* 7,000,000

TEN most successful Beatles singles.

	Song	*Year*
1	She Loves You	1963
2	I Want to Hold Your Hand	1963
3	Can't Buy Me Love	1964
4	Hey Jude	1968
5	Get Back	1969
6	Help!	1965
7	Ticket to Ride	1965
8	I Feel Fine	1964
9	Hello Goodbye	1967
10	The Ballad of John and Yoko	1969

A calendar day means the 24 hours from one midnight to the next.

A calendar month means any one of the twelve months of the year.

A calendar year means the period of time between 1 January and 31 December.

Thirty days have September,
April, June and November.
All the rest have thirty-one
Excepting February alone,
Which has just eight days and a score,
Till Leap Year gives it one day more.

The old Roman calendar had just ten months, which is why December, our twelfth month, means "tenth" in Latin.

Leap Years.

A year consists of roughly 365¼ days, so we add an extra day in leap years to even things up. In general, every fourth year is a leap year, but there is a slight inaccuracy which adds up to a whole day every 128 years. In 1582 Pope Gregory corrected this mistake by excluding century years from leap years unless you can divide them by 400. (So 2000 will be a leap year). The modern calendar is still called the Gregorian Calendar in his honour.

The twelve months of the year and how they got their names.

JANUARY: From the Latin Januarius. Janus was the two-faced god of entrances and exits.

FEBRUARY: From the Latin Februarius. Februare means to purify, and 15 February was the Roman Day of Purification.

MARCH: From the Latin Martius, alias Mars,

the Roman God of War.

APRIL: From the Latin Aprilis, the month sacred to Venus, the Roman goddess of love.

MAY: From the Latin Maius. Maia was a Roman goddess.

JUNE: From the Latin Junius, possibly in honour of the Roman goddess Juno.

JULY: From the Latin Julius, in honour of Julius Caesar, who introduced leap years to the calendar. Originally July was called Quintilis, the fifth month.

AUGUST: From the Latin Augustus, in honour of the Emperor Augustus. Originally August was called Sextilis, the sixth month.

SEPTEMBER: From the Latin septem, meaning seven. Nowadays, however, it is the ninth month.

OCTOBER: From the Latin octo, meaning eight.

NOVEMBER: From the Latin novem, meaning nine.

DECEMBER: From the Latin decem, meaning ten.

The seven days of the week and how they got their names.

The days of the week seem to have been an Anglo-Saxon invention and all their names except Saturday are Anglo-Saxon too.

SUNDAY: From Sunnen daeg, meaning the day of the sun.

MONDAY: From Monan daeg, meaning the day of the moon.

TUESDAY: From Tiwes daeg, named after Tiw, the god of war.

WEDNESDAY: From Wodnes daeg, after Woden, the chief of the gods.

THURSDAY: From Thunres daeg, after Thor, the thunder god. (The German for Thursday is actually Donnerstag, meaning day of thunder).
FRIDAY: From Frige daeg, after Frigg or Freya, the goddess of love.
SATURDAY: From Saeter daeg, named after the Latin, Saturni died, Saturn's day.

Monday's child is fair of face,
Tuesday's child is full of grace.
Wednesday's child is full of woe,
Thursday's child has far to go.
Friday's child is loving and giving,
Saturday's child works hard for a living,
While the child who is born on the Sabbath Day
Is blithe and bonny and good and gay!

Horoscopes.

The twelve signs of the Zodiac.

ARIES: The Ram, 21 March-April 20
TAURUS: The Bull, 21 April-21 May
GEMINI: The Twins, 22 May-21 June
CANCER: The Crab, 22 June-22 July
LEO: The Lion, 23 July-23 August
VIRGO: The Virgin, 24 August-22 September
LIBRA: The Scales, 23 September-23 October
SCORPIO: The Scorpion, 24 October-22 November
SAGITTARIUS: The Archer, 23 November-21 December
CAPRICORN: The Goat, 22 December-20 January
AQUARIUS: The Water Carrier, 21 January-18 February
PISCES: The Fish, 19 February-20 March

Western horoscopes group people according to their date of birth, which means that in theory

one twelfth of the world's population will have
a pleasant surprise next Thursday.

Chinese Horoscopes.

Chinese people believe in a twelve-year cycle.
Each year is named after an animal.

Rat
1900 1912 1924 1936 1948 1960 1972 1984
Buffalo
1901 1913 1925 1937 1949 1961 1973 1985
Tiger
1902 1914 1926 1938 1950 1962 1974 1986
Cat
1903 1915 1927 1939 1951 1963 1975 1987
Dragon
1904 1916 1928 1940 1952 1964 1976 1988
Snake
1905 1917 1929 1941 1953 1965 1977 1989
Horse
1906 1918 1930 1942 1954 1966 1978 1990
Goat
1907 1919 1931 1943 1955 1967 1979 1991
Monkey
1908 1920 1932 1944 1956 1968 1980 1992
Rooster
1909 1921 1933 1945 1957 1969 1981 1993
Dog
1910 1922 1934 1946 1958 1970 1982 1994
Pig
1911 1923 1935 1947 1959 1971 1983 1995

RATS are warm-hearted and quick-witted,
with good business sense.
BUFFALOES are strong, energetic and reliable
and can be very stubborn.
TIGERS are brave and proud and full of ideas.
CATS are artistic and sensitive, comfort-loving
and full of fun.

DRAGONS are determined and hard-working, but do not like routine.

SNAKES are intelligent and thoughtful and cling tightly to those they love.

HORSES are practical and independent. They love freedom and hate to be bored.

GOATS are gentle and artistic and enjoy the good things in life.

MONKEYS are intelligent and amusing, with good business sense and a gift for persuading people.

ROOSTERS are self-assured, frank and talkative, also very well-organised.

DOGS are honest and faithful, eager to please and very home-loving.

PIGS are wise and honest, fond of smart clothes, well-organised and very generous.

Which animal are you? Look at the chart to find out.

KINGS and Queens of England from 1066.

Generations of schoolchildren have learned rhymes to remind them. Here is just one of those rhymes.

Billy, Billy, Henry, Steve,
Henry, Dick, John, Henry Three.
Three Teds, then Richard Two,
Three more Henries — then what's new?
Two more Teds, then Dick the Bad,
Two more Henries, Ted the Lad.
Mary, Bess and Silly Jim,
Charles — but they beheaded him!
One more Charles, then Jamie Two;
Bill-and-Mary; Anne — then who?
Four Georges, Billy, then Victoria —
These little lists were sent to bore ya!
Ted the Seventh liked his fun,
Georgie was the quiet one.
Ted was an abdicator reckoned,
Then came George and Bess the Second.

TEN busiest airports in the world.

	Airport	Country/State	Passengers per annum
1	Chicago-O'Hare	Illinois	53,338,056
2	Atlanta	Georgia	45,191,480
3	Los Angeles	California	41,417,867
4	Dallas/Fort Worth	Texas	39,945,326
5	London-Heathrow	England	34,700,000
6	Denver	Colorado	34,685,944
7	Newark	New Jersey	29,433,046
8	San Francisco	California	28,607,363

| 9 | New York-JFK New York | 27,223,733 |
| 10 | Tokyo | Japan | 27,217,761 |

LOST Property.

Over 130,000 items of lost property are found on London Underground trains and buses every year. Here are the ten most common items handed in during 1987-88:

1 Umbrellas (23,250)
2 Handbags, purses, etc (19,868)
3 Books (19,329)
4 Items of Clothing (15,211)
5 Cases and Bags (9,317)
6 Keys (9,265)
7 Spectacles (5,574)
8 Cameras, Radios and Jewellery (5,304)
9 Pairs of Gloves (4,402)
10 Odd Gloves (1,600)

and the most unusual:

False Teeth
Bag of Human Bones
TV set
Stuffed Gorilla
Box of Glass Eyes
Bed
Artificial Hand
Garden Bench
Metre-long Spanner
Outboard Motor

AN ABC of Unusual Currencies.

Albania: *100 qindarka = 1 lek*
Bangladesh: *100 paise = 1 taka*
China: *100 fen = 1 yuan*
Dominican Republic: *100 centavos = 1 peso*
Ecuador: *100 centavos = 1 sucre*
Finland: *100 penniä = 1 markka*

Gambia: *100 bututs = 1 dalasi*
Hungary: *100 fillér = 1 forint*
Iceland: *100 aurar = 1 króna*
Jordan: *1,000 fils = 1 dinar*
N Korea: *100 jun = 1 won*
Laos: *100 ats = 1 kip*
Macao: *100 avos = 1 pataca*
Nigeria: *100 kobo = 1 naira*
Oman: *1,000 baiza = 1 rial*
Papua New Guinea: *100 toea = 1 kina*
Qatar: *100 dirhams = 1 riyal*
Romania: *100 bani = 1 leu*
Sweden: *100 ore = 1 krona*
Tonga: *100 senite = 1 pa'anga*
Uganda: *100 cents = 1 shilling*
Vietnam: *10 hào or 100 xu = 1 dông*
Yugoslavia: *100 paras = 1 dinar*
Zambia: *100 ngwee = 1 kwacha*

TEN Most Valuable Properties in Monopoly.

	ATLANTIC CITY	VALUE/£	LONDON
1	Boardwalk	400	Mayfair
2	Park Place	350	Park Lane
3	Pennsylvania Avenue	320	Bond Street
4	N Carolina Avenue	300	Oxford Street
	Pacific Avenue	300	Regent Street
6	Marvin Gardens	280	Piccadilly
7	Atlantic Avenue	260	Coventry Street
	Ventnor Avenue	260	Leicester Square

9	Illinois Avenue	240	Trafalgar Square
10	Indiana Avenue	220	Fleet Street
10	Kentucky Avenue	220	Strand

THE world's tallest habitable buildings.

	Building	Country	Storeys	m	ft
1	Sears Tower	Chicago, USA	110	443	1,454
2	World Trade Centre (twin towers)	New York City, USA	110	417	1,388
			110	415	1,362
3	Empire State Building	New York City, USA	102	381	1,250
4	Bank of China	Hong Kong	72	368	1,209
5	Standard Oil Building	Chicago, USA	80	346	1,136
6	John Hancock Center	Chicago, USA	100	344	1,127
7	Chrysler Building	New York City	77	319	1,046
8	Texas Commerce Plaza	Houston, USA	75	305	1,002
9	Allied Bank Plaza	Houston, USA	71	300	985
10	Columbia Center	Seattle, USA	76	291	954

JUNK FOODS

TEN Favourite Crisp Flavours.

1. Ready Salted
2. Cheese and Onion
3. Salt 'n' Vinegar
4. Bacon
5. Beef
6. Bovril
7. Chicken
8. Tomato Sauce
9. Gammon
10. Spring onion

Smith's Ten Best Selling Snacks.

1. Hula Hoops
2. Quavers
3. Square Crisps
4. Wotsits
5. Skips
6. Monster Munch
7. Snaps
8. Crispy Tubes
9. French Fries
10. Nik Naks

TEN Largest Dinosaurs.

	Name	Weight (Approx)	Height
1	Seismosaurus	80 tonnes	30-37m/ 94-120ft
2	Ultrasaurus	50 tonnes	31m/100ft

3	Antarctosaurus	80 tonnes	30m/98ft
4	Supersaurus	90 tonnes	25m/80ft
5	Diplodocus	60 tonnes	27m/88.5ft
6	Brachiosaurus	80 tonnes	25m/80ft
7	Barosaurus	60 tonnes	25m/80ft
8	Pelorosaurus	50 tonnes	24m/79ft
9	Mamenchisaurus	30 tonnes	22m/75ft
10	Apatosaurus	30 tonnes	20-21m/65-69ft

TEN countries with the highest girl guide/scout membership.

	Country	*Approx Membership*
1	United States	2,917,500
2	Philippines	1,597,000
3	United Kingdom	750,500
4	India	442,150
5	Canada	269,000
6	Korea	144,500
7	Indonesia	99,000
8	Japan	98,500
9	Australia	94,000
10	Pakistan	93,500

TEN countries with the highest scout membership.

	Country	*Approx Membership*
1	United States	3,825,000
2	Philippines	2,061,000
3	Indonesia	2,058,000
4	India	1,229,000
5	United Kingdom	681,250
6	Thailand	330,150
7	Bangladesh	312,250
8	Canada	304,150
9	Japan	285,000
10	South Korea	268,500

TEN tallest giants.

	Name	Nationality	Height	
			m	cm
			(ft	in)
1	Robert Pershing Wadlow	American	2 (8	72 11.11)
2	John William Rogan	American	2 (8	64 8)
3	John F. Carroll	American	2 (8	63.5 7.75)
4	Valno Myllyrinne	Finnish	2 (8	51.4 3)
5	Bernard Coyne	American	2 (8	48.9 2)
	Don Koehler	American	2 (8	48.9 2)
7	Patrick Cotter (O'Brien)	Irish	2 (8	46 1)
8	'Constantine' (1872-1902)	German	2 (8	45.8 0.8)
9	Gabriel Estavao Monjane	African	2 (8	45.7 0.75)
10	Sulaiman 'Ali Nashnush	Libyan	2 (8	45 0.4)

TEN places kids would most like to visit.

We did a survey in several school playgrounds. A surprising number of children said they preferred to stay at home and do their own thing, but here are the top ten destinations for the rest:

1 Disney World and EPCOT, Florida, USA
2 Cape Canaveral, Florida, USA
3 Disneyland, California, USA
4 New York, USA
5 The Eiffel Tower, Paris

6 East Africa on Safari
7 Alton Towers, UK
8 The London Dungeon, UK
9 Legoland, Denmark
10 Anywhere with lots of snow for skiing and
   tobogganing

TOP 10 film failures.

	Film	Year
1	The Adventures of Baron Munchausen	1988
2	Ishtar	1987
3	Inchon	1981
4	The Cotton Club	1984
5	Santa Claus — The Movie	1985
6	Heaven's Gate	1980
7	Pirates	1986
8	Rambo III	1988
9	Raise the Titanic	1980
10	Lion of the Desert	1981

TOP 10 most successful animated Films.

	Film	Year
1	Who Framed Roger Rabbit?	1988
2	Snow White and the Seven Dwarfs	1937
3	Jungle Book	1967
4	Bambi	1942
5	Fantasia	1940
6	Cinderella	1949

7	Lady and the Tramp	1955
8	The Little Mermaid	1989
9	101 Dalmatians	1961
10	Pinocchio	1940

TEN most successful science-fiction films.

	Film	*Year*
1	E.T.	1982
2	Star Wars	1977
3	Return of the Jedi	1983
4	Batman	1989
5	The Empire Strikes Back	1980
6	Ghostbusters	1984
7	Back to the Future	1985
8	Ghost	1990
9	Superman	1978
10	Close Encounters of the Third Kind	1977/80

TEN most successful comedy films.

	Film	*Year*
1	Beverly Hills Cop	1984
2	Tootsie	1982
3	Ghost	1990
4	Pretty Woman	1990
5	Three Men and a Baby	1987
6	Beverly Hills Cop II	1987
7	Home Alone	1990
8	The Sting	1973
9	National Lampoon's Animal House	1978
10	Crocodile Dundee	1986

TEN film rental blockbusters.

	Film	*Year*
1	E.T.	1982
2	Star Wars	1977
3	The Return of the Jedi	1983
4	The Empire Strikes Back	1980
5	Ghostbusters	1984
6	Jaws	1975
7	Raiders of the Lost Ark	1981
8	Indiana Jones and the Temple of Doom	1984
9	Beverly Hills Cop	1984
10	Back to the Future	1985

TOP 10 consumers of baked beans worldwide.

	Country	Retail Sales £
1	United Kingdom	105,000,000
2	Sweden	610,000
3	Greece	290,000
4	West Africa	272,000
5	Spain	250,000
6	West Germany	213,000
7	Dubai	141,000
8	Bahrain	102,000
9	Kuwait	78,000
10	Saudi Arabia	77,000

TEN Most Expensive Toys sold at Sotheby's.

		£
1	Character doll, German, 1909	90,200
2	Wooden doll, English, 1690	67,000
3	Teddy bear, German, 1920	55,000
4	Tinplate battleship, German, 1904	39,600
5	Tinplate paddleboat, German, 1902	28,600
6	Tinplate Gauge I train, German, 1909	28,050
7	Gauge I armoured train set, German, 1902	26,400
8 =	Baby house, English, 1675	25,300
8 =	Tinplate riverboat, German, 1912	25,300
10 =	Character doll, German, 1909	24,200
10 =	Teddy bear, German, 1912	24,200

FIRST ten people in space.

		Country	Date	Duration hr min	Spacecraft
1	Fl Major Yuri Alekseyevich Gagarin	USSR	12 April 1961	1.48	Vostok 1
2	Major Gherman Stepanovich Titov	USSR	6-7 August 1961	25.18	Vostok II
3	Lt Col John Herschel Glenn	USA	20 February 1962	4.56	Friendship 7
4	Lt Col Malcolm Scott Carpenter	USA	24 May 1962	4.56	Aurora 7
5	Major Andrian Grigoryevich Nikolayev	USSR	11-15 August 1962	94.22	Vostok III
6	Col Pavel Romanovich Popovich	USSR	12-15 August 1962	70.57	Vostok IV
7	Cdr Walter Marty Schirra	USA	3 October 1962	9.13	Sigma 7
8	Major Leroy Gordon Cooper	USA	15-16 May 1963	34.19	Faith 7
9	Lt Col Valeri Fyodorovich Bykovsky	USSR	14-19 June 1963	119.6	Vostok V
10	* Jr Lt Valentina Vladimirovna Tereshkova	USSR	16-19 June 1963	70.50	Vostok VI

* First woman in space.

And finally . . .
TEN Terribly Boring Facts.

1   Over 32 million new cars are built every year.

2   Boys may continue to grow until the age of 23, whereas most girls are fully grown by about 20.

3   British amateur gardeners grow more beetroot than any other vegetable.

4   You spend a third of your life in bed.

5   The biggest bell in the world is the 5.91m diameter Tsar Kolokol in Moscow. It was cracked before it could be installed and it stands, unrung, outside the Kremlin.

6   China grows nearly 2 million tons of tobacco a year.

7   The first country to give women the vote was New Zealand in 1883, but the Isle of Man led the world; Manx women were given the vote in 1880.

8   In the Falkland Islands there are 368 sheep for every human being.

9   Russia and Republics has 2495 daily newspapers with a total circulation of nearly 258,000,000 each day.

10 The longest film ever screened was called *The Longest and Most Meaningless Movie in the World* (UK, 1970) and lasted 48 hours. It was not a success.